The Bear
and the Bees

An Aesop's Fable
Retold by Annette Smith
Illustrated by Pat Reynolds

A long time ago,
a big brown bear
crawled out of his cave
and into the bright sunlight.

He had been asleep all winter.
Now it was spring again,
and he was very hungry indeed.

2

3

The bear plodded along
through the forest,
eating new green leaves
from the bushes.

Insects and mice
and ground squirrels
ran about in the long grass.

4

One little ground squirrel
put its head up out of the rocks,
but quickly disappeared
down into its hole
when it saw the bear.

By now, the bear was feeling
more and more hungry.
He was feeling grumpy, too.

A few leaves and insects
were not enough food
for a large brown bear.
He had to find
something else to eat soon.

He made his way down to the river.
A fish would make a good meal.

But, just as the bear caught a fish,
a bee began to buzz round his head.

The bear shook his head,
and the fish slipped out of his paw.
The bee buzzed round
the bear's head again.
This time, it stung him
right on the end of his nose.

The bear was angry.
He didn't like being stung
on the nose,
and he didn't like losing his meal.

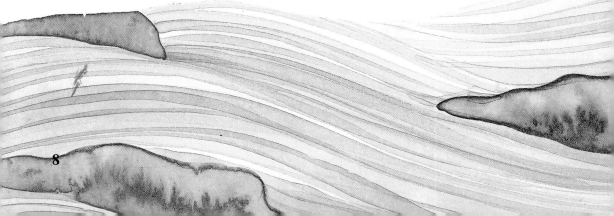

The bear was so angry,
that he chased the bee.
He ran through the long grass
and into the forest.

The bee disappeared
into a hollow log.

The bear began to attack the log.
He scratched and clawed
at the rotten wood
until he had pulled it apart.
He was going to **get** that bee!

But lots of bees had made a nest
in the hollow log.

They were very annoyed
when the bear broke their nest.
They flew out of the log
and buzzed crossly
round and round the bear's head.

The bear stood up
on his two back legs
and hit out at the bees.
But they just kept on diving
and buzzing round his head.

The bees stung the bear
on his long nose.
They flew into his ears and mouth,
and they even stung him on his tongue!

The bear had to get away fast.
There was only one thing
that he could do to save himself.

The bear ran back down to the river
and rushed into the water.
Some of the bees followed him,
but he stayed under the water
until they had gone.

15

That day,
the bear learned a lesson
he would never forget.

He shouldn't have let
one small thing make him angry.
Then he wouldn't have been hurt
so badly.